101
STORIES
OF
GRAND MOTHER

THIS BOOK
BELONGS TO
_____

ARORA'S

Published by :

Arora Book Company

109, Prakash Mahal, Ansari Road,
Near Bal-Gopal Restaurant
Darya Ganj, New Delhi-110002.
Ph. : 325-7092, 325-7964

(All Rights Reserved by the Publishers)

Photo Composing by :

Sarvpriya

13-14, Nirankari Colony, Delhi-9
Tel. : 7125617

Retold By : S. Bhatia .

Illustrated By : G. Gopal

Processing by : BEST PHOTOLITHOGRAPHERS

Price Rs. 99-00

First published 1990, Reprinted 1991, 1992, 1993, 1994, 1995, 1996, 1997,
1998, 1999, 2000, 2001, 2002

CONTENTS

The Wolf and the Lamb

A wolf spied a lamb who was drinking out of a stream and began to think of an excuse to attack it and eat it.

'You are making my part of the stream dirty,' accused the wolf.

'How can that be?' said the lamb. 'You are further upstream than me and the water flows down, not up.'

'Aren't you the lamb who insulted my father last year?' asked the wolf.

'I wasn't even born last year,' came the reply.

'Enough of all this talk,' snarled the wolf. 'I am not going to miss a chance of eating you just because you are good at excuses.'

7

The Ox and the Horse

The ox and the horse realised that their master was preparing to depart for the war. The horse was very worried when it thought about the dangers it would have to face up in a battle. The ox, on the other hand, was extremely cheerful in the belief that, in the absence of the master, he would have less work to do.

All this changed a shortwhile later, when the news arrived that the enemy had already surrendered. To celebrate the great victory, the cavalryman held an enormous banquet with plenty of roast meat: who was the loser then, do you think?

The Farmer and His Sons

A farmer, who realised that he was on his deathbed, called his sons to him.

'I am about to leave you,' he murmured, 'but I have something for you. Dig up the vineyard and share everything you find there.'

The sons thought that the father had meant a hidden treasure and thus, the moment he died, they began to hoe and dig at a furious pace. They did not find any treasure, for there was none to find, but the earth in the vineyard, hoed and dug so thoroughly, produced that year an enormous quantity of excellent grapes.

The Monkey and the Fishermen

Two fishermen were throwing their nets into the river and a monkey on the branches of a tree watched their actions with interest. At midday, the men went off to eat and left their nets on the river-bank, intending to use them again after lunch.

The monkey came down from the tree, picked up one of the nets and tried to throw it as he had seen the men do. The only thing it succeeded in doing, however, was to imprison itself completely in the tight netting.

'Now,' said the monkey, 'I have learnt that it is better to leave that task to those who know how to do it.'

The Sick Lion

Once the lion had very bad indigestion and all the doctors in the forest visited him

'What bad breath you have, your majesty!' exclaimed the zebra.

'How dare you!' said the indignant lion and knocked down the zebra.

'What a pleasant smell!' said the hyena, who had seen what had happened to the zebra.

'Do you think I'm stupid?' roared the angry lion, and killed the hyena as well. 'And what do you think?' the lion asked the fox. 'Unfortunately, your majesty,' replied that shrewd animal, 'my nose is completely blocked with a clod and I can smell nothing!'

The White Snake and the Black Snake

One day, King Solomon was out hunting, when he noticed two snakes engaged in a fight.

The larger snake was white and shining. The other was smaller and black with long, poisonous fangs. Just as the black snake was about to give its opponent a fatal bite, the king grabbed up a stone and killed it. Safe at last, the white snake went off into the trees.

Some time later, the king was confronted by a giant who appeared out of the forest. Solomon was very frightened, but the giant reassured him. He told him that he was the white snake that Solomon had helped earlier and he explained that the black snake was an enemy who had been trying to poison him. In the course of their battle, both had changed into snakes.

'To show my thanks for your help,' the giant went on, 'I would like to offer you a gift. Would you prefer a gift of gold or a gift of healing?'

'I'm already rich enough,' replied the king 'and the other gift would be more suitable for a doctor.'

'Well, what do you want?' asked the giant. 'Wisdom,' replied the king.

'You shall have it in abundance,' promised the

giant. And that was how King Solomon became the wisest man in the world.

The Cat and the Hens

Acat had heard that all the hens in a chicken coop had fallen ill. He had been thinking for a long time of a way to get the coop door open and at last this seemed like a very good opportunity.

He dressed up as a doctor, with a bag full of instruments and medicines and off he went to the chicken coop.

'Good day, hens, how are you feeling? I've come to give you a check up. Please open the door.'

But the chickens all answered together: 'Thanks very much, but we'll all feel a lot better if you would just go away, thank you.' Because, "Wisdom is greater than strength."

The Sick Lion and the Prudent Fox

When the lion was old and tired, realised that, if he still wanted to get enough to eat, he would have to retort more to cunning and less to force. So he pretended to be sick and retired in his den. Then on every time one of his subjects came by, the lion would reach out with his paw, grab the visitor and ate him.

Thus came the fox's turn, but the fox remained at the entrance.

'Do come in, fox!' said the lion cordially. 'Thank you, but I'd really rather not,' the fox replied. 'Although I can see so many footprints going in, I cannot see one which comes out!' It is rightly said, "Well goes the case when wisdom counsels."

15

The Mad Fisherman

It was market day in the city and carts and animals had arrived from all over the countryside. There were pedlars and merchants, breeders and farmers, noblemen and clowns. Even the arrival of the king was expected.

In the stable, a young foal was born. But as soon as it was able to stand, it fled in terror from all the noise and excitement and hid between two oxen who were pulling a plough.

The owner of the foal wanted his animal back, but the owner of the oxen said: 'The foal is mine, because it has chosen for itself.' They took their dispute to the king, who decided that the foal should remain where it was, as if the two oxen had become its parents from the moment the foal itself had chosen them.

The next day, when the king was out in his carriage, he came across the first owner of the foal standing in the middle of the street with a fishing net. He was casting his net as if he were fishing to the amusement of everyone around.

'What on earth are you doing?' the king asked him.

'I'm fishing, your majesty,' replied the man. 'If two oxen can be parents to a foal, why shouldn't I be able to catch fish in the middle of the street?'

The Fox and Wolf in Court

The wolf accused the fox of having cheated him; the fox, in turn, accused the wolf of having robbed him. They took their dispute to court and it fell to the monkey to judge the issue. Unfortunately, the whole case was so full of contradictions that no-one could make head or tail of it. Finally the monkey lost his patience.

'The wolf is guilty because he falsely accused the fox,' he decided 'and the fox is guilty because we all know he is a thief by nature. And since the right place for both liars and robbers in prison, it is to prison that I will send them both !'

The Dog and the Donkey

The dog was awakened by a noise, but went back to sleep at once.

'Why don't you bark?' asked the amazed donkey. 'It could be thieves!'

'You would be better advised to mind your own business,' he told the donkey. The indignant donkey began to bray as loudly as he could. He frightened off the thieves and caused the master to come running. The master was so furious at being woken up that he began to beat the donkey.

I warned you, said the experienced old dog afterwards: 'With a master like that, it is better to think only of yourself, first and foremost.'

How Deserts Are Formed

On the day of creation, the whole world was one huge garden of flowers. The Lord, however, called man to him and gave him this warning:

'Beware, every time you do something wrong a grain of sand will fall on the earth.'

But mankind paid no attention at all to this warning.

'What harm could a few grains of sand do?'

They continued to do wicked things and thus, little by little, the world has been invaded by the rivers and the seas of sand, which form the great deserts.

20

The Hare and the Fox

'What are you staring at?' said a fox to a hare who was observing him.

'I was wondering,' said the hare, 'if you really are as cunning as people say, or is it that you just take advantage of the foolishness of the others?'

'That's an interesting question,' replied the fox. 'Why don't you come to my house and we can discuss it over dinner?'

When the hare reached the fox's house, he realised, although, the table was set, there was no food on it, so he ran off at once.

Can you guess what the fox was planning for dinner?

The Donkey's Skin

There was once a rich and powerful king who, though old and ugly, made up his head to marry a young, beautiful girl at the court. The girl did not want to marry the king and asked her stepmother for help to escape from this marriage.

'You can never say no to the king,' said the woman, 'but you can lay down absurd conditions. Ask him for the skin of his donkey.'

Since this donkey was a magic donkey, on which all the king's power depended, so the two of them never dreamed for one moment that he would make such a sacrifice. But the king at once sent the girl what she had asked for.

The young girl decided to run away. She put on the donkey skin, so she would not be recognised and fled to a nearby country. To earn herself a living, there, she took the job of a serving girl in an inn: and indeed she was good at everything she did, especially baking cakes. She never took off her disguise and though it made her look horrible, the donkey skin kept her safe. Occasionally when she was alone in her room, she washed and combed her hair and put on the fine dress she had brought with her.

One day, the son of the king of that land happened to come to the inn. Looking around the place, he found a locked door. Out of curiosity he peeped through the keyhole and saw such a beautiful young girl that he fell in love at first sight. When he asked who stayed in that room, he was told that it was only an ugly serving girl.

When Donkey Skin was shown to him, he was forced to admit that it was not the girl he had seen through the keyhole. The prince grew lovesick and lost his appetite. As he grew weaker, the court doctor decided that he could only be tempted to eat again by a piece from one of Donkey Skin's delicious cakes. So she was commanded to bake a cake, but when the prince took his first bite he found in it a ring, which had slipped from Donkey Skin's finger. See Page 39

The Cricket and the Ants

It was summer and the cricket sat on an ear of wheat happily singing and enjoying the sun.

He felt extremely sorry for the ants, who worked ceaselessly, looking for grains of wheat to take back to their store.

Poor things, they really did not know-how to enjoy life.

But soon the winter came and the thoughtless cricket had no food at all to eat.

He would surely have died of hunger if it had not been for the generous ants who had given him some of their grain. "Think of keeping something for the rainy days."

24

The Hunting Dog and the Guard Dog

A man had two dogs and he trained one as a hunter and the another as a guard dog; whenever the hunting dog caught some game, the tastiest morsels were always given to the guard dog.

One day the hunter protested to the guard dog: 'It's not fair. I work at hunting all day long and you get your food without doing anything.'

'That must be the way the master wants it,' replied the guard dog.

'Obviously it is more important for him to reward the dog who protects his home than the one who goes out hunting.'

25

The Fox and the Monkey King

All the animals of the forest gathered to elect their new king.

They chose the monkey because they were amused by his antics. The fox was very disappointed at not being chosen and waited for a chance to get it.

One day, he found a piece of meat on a path. He realised at once it was the bait for a trap. But off he went to the monkey and offered to show him where it was, as a sign of his loyalty. The monkey king at once fell into the trap and the fox burst out laughing.

'With so few wits, you cannot even rule yourself; let alone animals.'

The Eagle and the Crow

A crow saw an eagle dropped down from the sky on to a lamb, caught it with its claws and flew straight back with it to its nest.

The crow thought he would like to do the same.

But the lamb was much too heavy for him and what was worse, the crow's little claws got caught in the lamb's thick fur, so the bird was trapped there.

The shepherd saw the crow, caught it and put it in a cage.

So the one who thought to imitate an eagle ended up being laughed at by everyone. "Think before you act."

The Bell on the Cat

Several centuries ago, the mice called a meeting to consider their sad situation.

All the speakers agreed on the fact that it was the fault of the cats and they debated on the ways in which they could avoid being hunted by them.

Finally, a solution was proposed and everyone approved. It was decided to attach a bell to every cat so that the mice would hear them coming.

This law is still in force, but unfortunately no mice have come forward to volunteer to put the bells on the cats.

The Flowers from the Moon

High in the mountains lived a prince whose great wish was to journey to the moon, because he loved its gentle glow. His dream finally came true. When he reached the moon, he discovered its light comes from the moon king's beautiful daughter.

The two young people soon fell in love, but the worlds they came from were very different and soon they had to part. As a sign of her great love, the moon king's daughter gave the prince one of the smooth and lovely flowers that covered the moon like snow and this was how the first alpine flower was brought to earth.

The Lion and the Grateful Mouse

A lion was preparing to eat a mouse it had just caught. 'Let me go,' the mouse begged him, 'sooner or later you may need my help.'

The king of the forest found this idea so ridiculous that he laughed aloud, but he let the little mouse go anyway. Some time later, the lion was trapped in a net which had been set down by the hunters. Then along came the mouse, who chewed the netting and freed him.

'As you can see,' said the mouse, 'even the mighty sometimes need the help of the weak.'

30

The Fox and the Stork

In order to pay back a debt, the fox had to invite the stork over the dinner, even though he did not really want to. He made a tasty soup, but he served it up in a very shallow dish and the stork's long beak could hardly reach to get hold of any of it.

Like a true lady, the stork did not complain and even invited the fox to dinner with her. The stork in her turn cooked a delicious meal, but she served it in a tall narrow goblet that the fox could not even get his nose into. So he did not get anything to eat.

"If you play dirty tricks on people, then you must expect to have them played on you as well."

Stupid Catherine

When Stupid Catherine went out, she often forgot to close the door behind her. One day, she had to go out of the house to take some lunch for her husband, Joseph, who was always telling her: 'Don't forget the door.'

This time, Catherine thought deeply till an answer came to her.

The best way not to forget to close the door was to take it with her. So she took off its hinges and heaved it up onto her back. But then, what could she do with the heavy lunch basket?

'I know' she cried. 'I'll hang it on the door handle, so that the door has to carry it, not me.'

32

The Forest King Goes to War

King lion was getting ready to go to war and called all the other animals.

But his ministers asked him to dismiss the donkey and the rabbit, because one was too stupid and the other was too easily scared.

'Not at all,' refused the king. 'The donkey has a voice which is even more resounding than mine. He can be the trumpeter.'

'The rabbit, being so quick, will be invaluable for carrying messages,' added the king. To win a war you must know how to get the best out of everyone.

Metabo and Camille

King Metabo was a famous javelin thrower. One day he went out hunting with his young daughter, Camille.

All of a sudden the king was attacked by a band of enemies. He had to flee from them until he came to a fast flowing river, which he was unable to swim across because of his daughter on his back. It seemed as if he was lost until he thought of a way out.

Tying his daughter to his javelin, he hurled it with all his strength to the other side of the river; then he dived in himself and swam across to where Camille was. His enemies were so amazed that they gave up the chase.

The Fox without Tail

A fox lost her tail in a trap and was ashamed of her loss. It seemed extremely unfair to her that she alone should lack a tail.

She seriously thought that the world would be a much improved place if all the other foxes were to be without tails.

And so she tried to convince them all to cut off their tails.

'The tail,' she said, 'is just an extra weight. And you could hardly call it elegant! or pretty!'

'If that is so,' replied her friends, 'then why are you so unhappy without one?'

The Lion, the Wolf and the Fox

The lion was near to death and all the other animals tried to fawn on him, hoping to be named as his heir. The wolf tried to discredit the fox by telling the lion that the fox had not even bothered to visit the king. The fox arrived **just at** the right moment to overhear this.

'Who could love you more than me?' the fox asked the lion. 'For I have been all around the world, in search of the miraculous cure I bring you!'

'And what is it?' asked the lion.

'If you want to get well again, skin a live wolf', replied the fox, 'and wrap yourself in the fur while it is still warm!'

36

The Greedy Dog

One day, a dog stole a big piece of meat and proud of his own courage, ran off with it, held tightly in his jaws. He reached the bank of the river where he looked down and spied another dog with a piece of meat in its mouth, every bit as big as his own. He did not realise that it was merely his own reflection in the water. Feeling

greedy he threw himself on the other dog to steal his meat as well. Unfortunately, when he found himself in the water, he had to let go of his own piece of meat to avoid drowning and so was left with nothing. "So greediness proved a curse to him."

The Faithful Mongoose

Indu and Lav were a young Indian couple and they had a beautiful baby boy. One day, Indu said to her husband: 'You must look after the baby, while I go down to the river.' Lav sat down beside the pram and the baby fell asleep at once. A short time later, a messenger arrived from the royal palace and ordered Lav to follow him there to speak on behalf of a friend. Lav had to entrust the baby to the pet mongoose, which the young couple kept in the house. In India, people keep mongoose rather to keep cats; but where cats hunt mice, a mongoose does not hesitate to confront a snake. What is more, mongooses are more loyal than cats. The mongoose at once sat down to guard the baby. When a huge python entered by the window and approached the pram, the mongoose was ready for it and killed the python.

When Lav came back and found the mongoose, mouth and paws dripping with blood, he immediately thought the worst and beat the faithful animal. How surprised he was when he went into the house and found the baby sleeping peacefully and a huge python dead on the floor by the pram.

From that day on, the young couple loved the

courageous mongoose even more and Indu learnt that he should never doubt a faithful friend.

——— Contd. From Page 23 ———

The prince remembered having seen the ring through the keyhole on the beautiful young girl's finger. He vowed he would marry only the girl on whose finger the ring fitted perfectly. To make him happy, the king and the queen agreed to this, especially since a finger small enough to fit that ring must surely belong to a grand lady.

The search began at once and in the end even Donkey Skin was ordered to try the ring on. And then the 'ugly' serving girl had no trouble at all in proving that not only the ring belonged to her but that she really was the most beautiful young girl, the prince had seen at the inn. Everything was soon sorted out and a grand wedding took place that very same day.

The wolf and the Shepherd

Once a wolf got into the habit of following a flock of sheep without ever attacking any of them. As a result, after some time the shepherd began to think of the wolf as more of a guardian than an enemy.

One day the shepherd had to go to the city on business and it seemed natural for him to leave his flock in the care of the wolf. When he returned that evening, every single one of his sheep had been killed. The shepherd thought long and hard over what had happened and in the end realised, that it was completely his own fault.

'Whoever puts his faith in wicked friends should expect no better.'

The Lion and His Partners

The goat, the sheep and the cow went into business with the lion and just as in every company, it was agreed that costs and profits would be divided equally. It happened that they trapped a deer and held a shareholders' meeting in order to apportion it out. In fact, the lion was most meticulous about dividing the catch into four equal parts. 'I shall take the first share,' he said, 'because it is my right to do so being King of the Forest. I shall also take the second and also the third, because I'm the strongest. Should you lay claim to the rest, then I shall make a meal of you as well!'

The Princess and the Peas

O ne day a young beautiful girl arrived at the palace, claiming she was a princess.

The queen had made ready a room for her. And to put her to the test, she placed two peas under the bed and over it she put twenty mattresses and twenty featherdown covers.

In the morning, when the young girl woke up, she was aching all over and covered with bruises because of the peas. Such a delicate and sensitive skin confirmed her claim to be a princess and the queen considered her to be a suitable bride for the young prince, the heir.

The Madonna's Cup

A long long time ago, a heavy wagon was stucked in the mud and the wagon driver was unable to free it. Just then, by sheer chance, the Madonna passed by.

'I am thirsty,' she said. 'Give me a drink and I will set your wagon free.'

'Willingly,' said the man, offering her the bottle, 'but I don't have a cup.'

'I can provide the cup,' said the Madonna. And she broke off a white flower, with red stripes, in the shape of a chalice and she used it to drink from. Ever since then, people have called the flower of the convolvulus, 'The Madonna's Cup.'

The Two Mules

Two mules were on the same path. The first, who worked for a miller, was loaded with oats. The other was owned by a banker and was carrying a chest full of golden coins. Because of this it trotted along very proudly, full of itself.

But on hearing the clinking, some robbers realised that it was carrying a treasure.

They stole it and beat the mule badly with sticks.

'You see,' explained the first mule. 'Being rich and important has its drawbacks.'

The Fox and the Turtle

For want of a better meal, a starving fox once captured a turtle, but it could not manage to breakthrough the solid shell in order to eat it.

'You should try by putting me in the water for a while to soften me up,' suggested the shrewd turtle.

This sounded an excellent advice to the fox. He carried his prey to the stream and immersed it in the currents. The turtle, who was a superb swimmer, slid out of the fox's paws and re-emerged in the mid-stream laughing, 'There are animals who are even more cunning than you. Now you'll stay hungry!'

Why the Sun and the Moon Live in the Sky?

A long time ago, the Sun and the Moon were a married couple who lived on the Earth and were great friends of the Sea. One day, they invited the Sea to visit them but the Sea hesitated, thinking that there might not be enough room in their house. But they reassured him.

So the Sea went along with the fish and all the members of his family. Immediately the water began to rise and the Sun and the Moon, to avoid being drowned, had to climb up onto the roof and then eventually into the sky, where they are ever since.

Bondo the Wolf and the Stray Dog

Poor old Bondo, the wolf, was always getting into trouble; but when he met a stray dog, chased away from home and reduced to skin and bones from hunger, Bondo yelped with joy.

'Now I'm going to make a meal of you,' he said.

'Skinny as I am?' answered the dog, 'You'd be better off fattening me up a bit, first.'

Bondo the wolf thought this was a good idea; but by the time that the dog had become fat enough to eat, he had also become strong enough to frighten the wolf away, just by baring his teeth.

47

The Honest Woodcutter

Inder was so poor that he owned nothing except the axe he needed to earn his living as a woodcutter. One day, by a stroke of ill fortune, while he was working on the bank of a river, the blade of his axe flew off the handle and sank into the river. Poor Inder was desperately unhappy; now how could he cut the wood which had always earned him the little food that he ate?

His heart felt sighs were overheard by a strange, old man. As soon as he was told what had happened, the old man dived into the river and re-emerged a few moments later holding up a golden hatchet.

'Is this the one you lost?' he asked.

'No, that's not my hatchet,' Inder replied.

The old man dived into the water again and came up holding a silver hatchet. 'No, that's not mine either,' the woodcutter confirmed. On the third occasion, the old man came out holding Inder's blade. 'Yes, that's mine!' laughed the happy woodcutter.

'Take it. You owe me nothing for the help I have given you. Rather, since you have shown yourself to be neither greedy nor dishonest, you deserve to be rewarded. You can also keep both the golden and the silver axes!'

The Two Cockerels and the Eagle

There were once two cockerels. Both wanted to rule the roost in the farmyard and they decided to resolve the question, once and for all, by fighting a duel. They both fought bravely, but, in the end, one had to give up and ran away. The winner flew up onto a little wall and launched its triumphant, 'Cock-a-doodle-doo.'

Unfortunately, the noise attracted the attention of an eagle, which swept down and raked the cockerel with its claws. From this, we see that God gives grace to the humble **and He** does not hesitate to punish those who are too proud.

The Grocer's Shop

Charles could not keep count of the times he would stop and look in the window of the grocer's shop. That attractive sight looked even more enchanting now that it was Christmas time. What delicious foods were there on the great wooden table! An enormous turkey took pride of place in the middle and it was circled by

roast geese, hams and strings of sausages. Over the rest of the table there were cake stands of multi-hued marzipan fruits, huge sweet chestnuts, toffees, apples and sugared pears. In the air, there was a faint aroma of punch which warmed the little boy's heart.

The Peacock and the Crane

The peacock would often laugh at the crane, which, according to the peacock, had very drab plumage indeed. 'I am dressed in gold and purple,' the vain bird would say to the crane, 'while you have absolutely nothing of any beauty on your wings at all.'

'On the other hand,' the crane replied, 'I can sing to the stars while I fly high in the heavens, while you must drag yourself along the ground like the chickens in the farmyard!'

Perhaps, then it is better to be illustrious in poor clothes, rather than live without glory into a show of wealth.

The Miser and the Beggar

A poor man, who was reduced to rags, begged a rich Arab for some clothes; and since he had been asked in the name of Allah, the rich man could not refuse, but made sure he gave the beggar his oldest suit. The beggar put it on and according to custom, hung a sign on the collar stating, 'There is no god but Allah.'

'Are you not going to add', "And Mohammed is his Prophet"? asked the rich man, 'because they were the traditional words.'

'No,' the beggar replied, 'because when they made this suit, the prophet hadn't even been born yet.'

The Frog and the Ox

A frog decided to become as big as an ox.

So it began to breathe in and in and every time it swallowed more air, it did in fact to become bigger.

But it soon began to tire of its efforts.

'Am I big enough yet?' it asked hopefully of its many watching companions.

Then they had another look at the ox and shook their heads, 'No, a bit more.'

So the ambitious frog kept on puffing itself up and up.....until it burst like a balloon! "Do not make fool of yourself to make others merry."

The Silly Wolf and the Billy Goat

An old wolf was no longer as strong or as cunning as it used to be and the other wolves thought it was just plain silly sometimes. One of these times it was chasing a billy goat which jumped up on a high rock to save her.

'Why do you waste time chasing me?' the goat asked the silly wolf. 'If you want to catch me, just open your mouth wide and I'll jump into it.' The wolf obliged and the goat jumped, not into the wolf's mouth, but onto its head, landing so hard that the wolf was knocked out. When the wolf woke up with its mouth open, it could not recall if it had eaten the goat or not.

55

The Fearful Hunter and the Woodcutter

Do you know that many men are very brave while they are talking and are very scared when the time comes to act?

There was once a hunter who was going through the woods in search of a bear. He met a woodcutter and asked: 'My good man, do you happen to have seen the footprints of a bear?'

'Yes, I have seen them,' said the woodcutter, setting down his axe, 'and I will take you to its den.'

The hunter went **pale** with fear and started to shake. 'Thank you, but that won't be necessary,' he stammered. 'I am looking for tracks, not for the bears themselves!'

The Viper, the Water Snake and the Frogs

A viper often went to drink at a pond, which, the water snake claimed as his own. The two snakes decided to settle the matter by fighting. The frogs, eternal enemies of the water snake, supported the viper.

On the day of the contest, the frogs began to croak madly, for they could think of nothing else to do. The viper won the battle and afterwards the frogs asked the victorious viper for their share of the spoils. The viper began to whistle and the frogs were baffled.

'I'm repaying you in the same way you helped me,' explained the viper. "Do not poke your nose in the others affairs."

The Lion and the Ass

The lion had decided to go hunting and had chosen the ass as his companion, for he had thought of a way to make use of its distinctive braying.

The silly ass was extremely proud at being chosen as the lion's companion and with complete docility, he allowed the lion to dress him up in a cloak of leaves, thinking that this must be the correct hunting costume, whereas it was really only to be a disguise.

Following the lion's instructions, the ass went and stood in the middle of a meadow. At the agreed moment, the ass began to bray loudly and the deer were so terrified by the din that they fled on the way. And a few of them finished in the great paws of the lion or rushed straight into his huge jaws.

When the hunt was finished, the ass was quick to claim the credit for the great success of their joint venture. The lion, however, interrupted him at once: 'Be careful!' he growled. 'I might find that I have a taste for asses!'

The ass was wise enough not to press the point and left with his tail between his legs and nothing at all to show for his work.

The Horse and the Wolf

Once a horse was grazing in a field when he saw a wolf approaching. The frightened horse pretended it had a limp. Knowing that horses are strong, the wolf thought it would be cunning.

'Why are you limping?' asked the wolf.

'I've put my hoof on a thorn,' replied the horse. The wolf said, 'That looks like a serious wound. I've studied medicine. Perhaps you'd like me to look at it.' But as the wolf was bending to take hold of its leg, the horse gave it a mighty kick.

'Everyone knows his trade best,' thought the wolf, as he flew through the air.

The Distracted Astronomer

An astronomer was in the habit of going out every night to observe the stars; but no sooner he was outdoors, he was totally absorbed in the sights above him, that he did not look where he was putting his feet, so once he fell into a hole in the ground.

A passer-by heard his shouts and ran to help him. 'How do you hope to discover what's up in the sky,' he said to the astronomer, 'when you're not even capable of seeing what's under your nose?'

"Many men, while following their dreams, show themselves incapable of facing up to reality."

The Fox and the Geese

A fox jumped into a flock of geese, ready to eat them all. Feeling generous, he thought he would grant them a last desire.

'Please let us say our prayers, so we can die in peace,' they asked. The fox agreed and the first goose began to honk loudly with great feeling. It had not yet finished, when a second goose began to honk, followed by a third, then a fourth and then another and another.

And eventually the honking gave the fox such a bad headache that he decided to go home without any supper at all.

The Crow's Challenge

Two crows challenged each other to see which of them could fly highest, whilst carrying a sack of the same size.

The first crow filled his sack with cotton and laughed at the other crow who had filled his, instead with salt which was much heavier.

When, however, it began to rain, as the second crow had expected, the salt began to dissolve.

The cotton absorbed the rain water and became so heavy that the first crow did not even have the strength to get off the ground and he had to admit defeat.

The Lovelorn Lion and the Peasant

A lion was unfortunate enough to fall in love with the beautiful daughter of a peasant and he went to her father to ask for her hand in marriage. The peasant was worried about his daughter's future, but didn't have the courage to refuse the lion openly.

'My daughter,' he pretended, 'is allergic to teeth and claws. Come back after you have removed them and then you can marry her.'

The lovelorn lion promptly had his teeth and claws removed, but when he came back, he was absolutely harmless and the peasant beat him with a stick and chased him away.

The People's Faults

According to a Greek legend, when men were created, the great god Zeus gave each one a gift of two bags. One bag was full of man's own faults, the other full of everybody else's faults. But when the moment came for Zeus to give man his two bags, each one hanging at the opposite end of a carrying pole, by mistake he put the bag with the defects of everybody else in the front, whilst the bag with each man's own defects finished up behind his back.

It is for this reason, "It is too easy to see other people's faults but difficult to see our own!"

The Father and His Daughters

A man had two daughters, one was married to a poor farmer, the other to a potter. Once the father went to visit each of them and asked: 'How the business is going on?'

'Very well,' replied the first daughter, 'but we could use more water to irrigate the land. We pray every night that God will send us rain!' When he asked the second daughter, she replied: 'Business is going on well, but we pray to God for dry weather to harden our pots!' 'And what should I pray for?' exclaimed the father, 'if one daughter wants one thing and the other the opposite?'

The Fox and the Crow

One day a fox came across a crow who was perched on a branch with a piece of cheese in its beak. Immediately, the fox began to consider how he might obtain it for himself.

'You have everything; strength, beauty and wisdom!' he said flatteringly to the bird. 'If you only had a beautiful voice, then you would be perfect.'

Not wishing the fox to think that it did not have a fine voice, the crow began to sing. Of course, the piece of cheese fell from its beak and the fox claimed it at once. 'Your most serious problem,' laughed the fox, 'is that you have more vanity than intelligence!'

The Sick Camel

A camel who lived all alone on the edge of an oasis fell ill and all his relatives and friends visited him there.

Since the journey was a long one, they each stayed for a while to rest up and ate the grass that was growing around the oasis.

The camel was pleased to be visited, but when he felt better and roused himself to go and look for something to eat, he discovered that his friends and relatives had eaten everything. What could he do? There was no choice but to set off....and look for another oasis.

Silly Catherine

One day silly little Catherine went for a walk in the woods. When she reached the lake, she decided to eat, but then grew tired and slept till night time. When she woke up, it was so dark that she could not see her own reflection in the water.

'Am I really here or not?' she asked herself. She decided to go home and ask. When she got home she called out, 'Is Catherine there?'

'She must be in the bedroom,' replied a sleepy voice.

'If Catherine's at home,' thought Catherine, 'then I'm not Catherine.' So she went away and never returned.

The Old Woman and the Healer

An old woman whose eyes were inflamed called in a healer and he told her that the eyesight would become faultless again, provided she would pay a very expensive fee for his services. She agreed and he insisted her to keep her eyes shut during the treatment, at which time the healer stole all the old lady's furniture.

When he asked the woman for his fee, she refused to pay, so the healer took her to court. 'It's not true that he's made my eyes better,' the old lady told the judge. They have got worse. Before, I could see everything in my house, now I can't see at all.'

The Sun and the Wind

To see which was the stronger, the sun and the wind challenged each other to strip the clothes from the first passerby.

The wind puffed with all the air in its lungs; but the more it blew the more the man drew his clothes tight around him and feeling a bit cold he even pulled on a cloak.

The sun didn't do anything so strenuous; all it did was shine. And gradually the man grew hotter and hotter until he took off all his clothes to go for a swim.

Which just goes to show that gentle persuasion is more effective than violence.

The Two Friends

John and James were two friends who were crossing a forest, when, suddenly, they stumbled across a huge, black bear. Imagine how terrified they were! They attempted to flee but the bear chased them. John managed to climb up onto a tree. James, just as he was about to be caught, fell to the ground and pretended to be dead. He knew, "A bear only attacks something if it is alive."

The bear sniffed him all over, while the man tried to hold his breath as best as he could, hoping that the animal would not discover the pretence. In the end, after sniffing thoroughly, the bear must have thought that the man really was dead, because it ambled off on its huge paws.

With the danger over, John came down from the tree and as often happens after a big fright, he felt like making jokes. So he asked his friend, 'Well, what did the bear whisper into your ear?' But James was not in the same mood for jokes and he did not appreciate the question at all.

'The bear said,' he answered, looking John straight in the eye, 'It would be advisable for you not to travel again with a friend, who runs off and abandons you when danger threatens!' Because "A friend in need is a friend indeed."

Reynard the Fox and the Eels

A fisherman was returning home after a day by the river with his cart full of eels. Reynard the fox saw him and immediately thought of a way of getting himself a sumptuous dinner. He lay down in the middle of the road and pretended to be dead.

When the fisherman saw him, he fell for the trick. He picked up the fox, convinced that he had found himself a beautiful fox skin and put it on the back of his cart. Once on the move, Reynard emptied all the eels out into the road, gathered them up and ran off. So the gullible fisherman lost both, his fox fur skin and his fish.

The Fisherman and His Flute

There was once a fisherman who was also an excellent flute player. One day he took his flute and a fish-basket, jumped up on a rock and began to play his flute, convinced, the fish would be enchanted by his music and leap into the basket willingly. Unfortunately, he did not catch a single fish, so went home, collected his net and threw it into the water. He caught so many fish that his basket overflowed.

'Stupid creatures!' he exclaimed, as he watched the fish twist and jump in his net. 'You would not dance when I played my flute, but when I'm not playing, you can't stop dancing!'

The Fox and the Grapes

There was once a fox with an empty stomach, who went in search of something to eat. He chanced upon a vineyard, where large bunches of golden grapes hung from the vines above his head.

The fox jumped up and down, trying to bite into a bunch of the grapes, but he fell short. He tried again and again with all his might, but he still failed to reach the grapes. He was obliged to give up the attempt but consoled himself, as well as he could, by telling himself: 'It doesn't matter, because they weren't ripe yet.'

The Donkey in the Lion's Skin

A donkey **disguised** itself by dressing up as a lion and then went around spreading terror amongst the other animals.

Some time later, when it encountered a fox, the donkey roared as fiercely as it could, but the fox just burst out laughing.

'If I hadn't heard you braying, I might also have been scared by that lion's skin.'

There are a lot of stupid people, who, like the donkey, would like to dress up in fine clothes and pretend they are important, but they betray themselves.

The Owl and the Seagull

An owl and a Seagull went into business together. The owl did not have any money so he borrowed some. The seagull owned a precious jewel and he put that into the venture as well. The two of them went to board a ship, having decided to start their business in a far off land. But there was a storm and the ship sank. The owl and the seagull managed to get to safety; but they lost all of their possessions. Ever since then, the owl only comes out at night for fear of meeting its creditors and the seagull flies high over the rocks in the hope that the sea will give him back his precious jewel.

The Mosquito and the Bull

A mosquito landed on a bull's horn and there it settled down comfortably to make itself at home.

Only when it was time to leave, it remembered of its patient host, and it said to him:

'You'll be happy to know that I won't be disturbing you anymore; I'm going.'

'Me, happy!' replied the bull. 'I didn't feel you arrive and I did not even notice that you've gone.'

And that's the way it is.

"If someone is worth nothing then nobody cares whether he's there or not."

The Hen with the Silver Eggs

O ne day, in an Arabian city, a woman went to the market and bought a beautiful hen.

You can imagine her surprise, later when the hen laid a silver egg. If the hen could only be persuaded to lay more than one egg each day, the woman was sure she would never have to work again.

Therefore, the woman decided that the hen must eat more, so that it could lay more eggs.

But the only result was that the hen died of indigestion and did not lay any more eggs at all.

The Owl and the Nightingale

There was once a nightingale, in a cage by a window, who was in the habit of singing only at night. An owl was puzzled by this and went to ask the nightingale what the reason **was**?

'When I was captured,' explained the nightingale, 'it was day and I was singing. In this way I learnt to be more prudent to sing only at night.'

'Are you afraid, you might be captured a second time?' asked the baffled owl. 'It would have been better if you had been more careful the first time when your freedom was at risk. **Now** it doesn't really matter any-more!'

Redfeathers the Hen

Redfeathers, the hen, was so-called because all her feathers were red. One day the fox caught sight of her in the farmyard and his mouth began to water.

He ran home and told his wife to put on water for boiling a chicken and then he rushed back and before Redfeathers knew what was happening, she found herself snapped up inside a sack and was not even able to call for help.

Luckily, her friend the dove saw what had happened. She fluttered on to the path in the woods and lay there, pretending to have a broken wing. The fox was delighted to find that he would have a first course as well as a main dish. He put down the sack with the hen in it and chased off after the dove, who cleverly began to hop further and further away.

Redfeathers slipped out of the sack and put a stone in her place, then she too ran off. When the dove saw that her friend was safe, she flew up onto a tree. The fox then went back and picked up the sack, thinking that the hen was still in it. When the fox got home, he tipped the sack into the pot of boiling water, but the stone splashed it all over him and he burned his greedy paws.

The Right Bride

A young shepherd knew three girls, who were so beautiful that he did not know which one to marry. So he asked his mother for advice.

'Invite them to dinner,' she said, 'and watch how they cut the cheese.'

So he did.

The first girl ate the cheese with the rind still on; the second girl cut the rind, but she also cut off a good deal of edible cheese with it; the third girl took off exactly the right amount of rind and left all the edible cheese.

'Marry her,' said the mother, with certainty.

The Cockerel, the Cat and the Mouse

An inexperienced little mouse set off on a journey. He came across a cockerel. Never having seen one before, the little mouse was so afraid of the cockerel's beak, its feathers and red crest, that he ran off as fast as he could. Further on, the mouse saw a cat. What a handsome animal, he thought; what a soft fur, what striking eyes!

When the mouse got back home, he told his mother what he had seen.

'You silly mouse,' his mother said. 'Never go by appearances. The terrible animal that you saw was a harmless cockerel, while the fine looking one is our enemy, the cat.'

The Brother, the Sister and the Witch

A witch found two children playing beside a river and stole them away. They succeeded in escaping one day, but the witch set off to bring them back. A good fairy, who was passing by, saw the children and took pity on them. She set a great ring of fire around them to keep them safe; but the witch managed to blow out the flames.

So the fairy built round them a high wall of glass so smooth it could not be climbed. The witch returned to her house to find a hammer to break it with, but when she returned the fairy had spirited the children away and they were safe at home.

The Monkeys and the Bell

A thief, who was escaping with a stolen bell was killed and eaten by a tiger. The bell was found by the monkeys, who began to ring it. The noise frightened the people of the nearby villages, who thought it was the sound of a giant. Only one woman was not afraid and

she went out with a basket of fruit. Nearby she heard the bell, she left the basket on the ground and hid. No sooner had the monkeys thrown themselves on the fruit, the woman picked up the bell and ran back to the village. She was praised for her heroic courage...in stealing the bell from the giant!

The Friend's Pot

A woman asked to borrow a pot from her friend and handed it back the next morning, together with a much smaller pot.

'It is the son of your pot and was born during the night,' she explained. The friend was delighted to accept this. A few days later, the woman borrowed the pot

again, but this time she did not give it back. When the friend asked if she could have her pot back, the woman replied: 'It's dead.'

'A pot can't die,' her friend insisted.

'And why not?' the woman went on. 'If it can have a son, then it can surely die.'

The Patched-Up Boot

Castles, palaces, villas, houses, huts....how many different types of buildings we live in. Yet, I, who have been all over the world, can assure you that I have never seen a strange dwelling-place than the patched-up boot, in which I found a mother living with her children. All

the conversion work to make the boot comfortable and homely had been done by a master builder, who was a friend of the family. He had opened up thirteen windows and built a large balcony.

The children were noisy and a little wild: but in a house like that, how could they be expected to be good?

The Mystery of the Sphinx

A long long time ago, the city of Thebes was guarded by a sphinx, a creature with the head of a woman, the body of a lion and the wings of an eagle.

She asked the same riddle to every passer-by and when they could not answer, she consumed them.

'What being,' the sphinx asked Oedipus, when he came upon her, 'has four legs in the morning, two at midday and three in the evening?'

'Man,' answered Oedipus. 'As a child he crawls on all fours, in his prime he walks on two legs and when he is old he leans on a stick.'

The Sick Wolf and the Sheep

There was once a starving wolf in a sorry state. He had been obliged to flee from a pack of dogs and for many days he had found nothing to eat. He spied a little white sheep and thought: 'At last! Here is a meal for me!'

'Little white sheep,' he said to her, 'could you please bring me a drop of water from the river?, as you can see, I am very unwell. If you can bring me something to drink, I will be able to find something to eat.' 'But if I bring you something to drink,' said the little sheep, 'then you will already have found yourself something to eat!' and skipped off in the opposite direction.

The Fox and the Woodcutter

Long ago, a fox which was being chased by hunters took refuge in the house of a woodcutter and asked him to conceal her. The astonished man agreed, but when the hunters arrived, although, he said that he had not seen the fox, he tried to point out with dramatic gestures, the place where she was hiding. The hunters

paid no heed and went on their way. Afterwards, the fox came out of hiding and prepared to leave. 'Are you not even going to thank me?' complained the woodcutter. 'And should I thank you for what you said?' retorted the fox, 'Or for what you did?'

The Sun and the Moon

In the distant past, the moon used to be as bright as the sun.

This meant that mankind could not tell day from night, as it was always light.

There were all kinds of problems; people never knew when it was time to get up or when it was time to go to bed.

The Lord realised what was happening and at once ordered the Archangel Gabriel to spread his wings and veil the light of the moon.

And thus, the marks, which we see on the surface of the moon, are scratches made by the angel's long wings.

The Eagle and the Woodcutter

Once, a woodcutter found an eagle which was caught in a trap. He was so taken with the beauty and the majesty of the bird that he let it go free.

Some time later, the woodcutter sat down on a rock on the very top of a steep hill. While he was having his lunch, the eagle dropped like lightning from the sky and

flew away with his hat. The man automatically ran down the hill after the bird, just as the rock on which he had been sitting gave way with a loud crash.

Thus the grateful eagle had repaid its benefactor.

The Rose and the Amaranth

An Amaranth, which was growing beside a Rose, said one day: 'How beautiful you are, Rose! You are the delight of the gods and of men. I rejoice with you for your shapeliness and your perfume!'

'Oh, Amaranth,' the Rose replied, 'I live only for a few days and even if no-one picks me, I still wither and die. You, on the other hand, are always in flower and you live forever!'

Even today, the Amaranth is not sure if it is better or worse off than the Rose. Is it better to live for a long time or to be beautiful and glorious and live but briefly?

The Spiteful Gnomes

Once upon a time a woman had a lovely baby, but gnomes stole the child and put in its place a baby gnome in the cradle. The mother begged them to return the child to her, but they just laughed unkindly. Sad and distracted without her baby, the woman put a raw egg on

the fire instead of into the pot of water. The gnomes, who were always running around the kitchen, burst out laughing at this, because, as we all know, gnomes like to laugh more than anything else. So they returned the baby to her mother and took away the baby gnome.

Man and the Wolf

The wolf boasted that he was the strongest animal. The fox disagreed. 'Man in his prime is stronger!' 'Introduce me to one and we'll soon see,' retorted the angry wolf.

An old man went by. 'Is that a man?' asked the wolf. 'No, he is no longer in his prime,' replied the fox. A boy ran past. 'Is that one?' asked the wolf. 'No, he has not reached his prime,' the fox replied. Then a hunter appeared. 'That's him! That's a man!' exclaimed the fox. The wolf leapt out and was beaten by the hunter. 'Do you see?' asked the fox. 'Man has strengths which even you do not possess!'

The Frightened Cake

Once there was a mother who was always baking cakes for her children. One day she prepared a cake with so much love that when she took it out of the oven, even her spoilt children's mouths watered.

'Dear mother, kind mother,' her greedy and impatient children begged her, 'hurry up and give us a slice.'

'Wait until it cools down and you can eat it all,' was the reply.

But when the cake heard the fate that was in store for it, was terrified. The cake jumped out of the dish, rolled off like a wheel, out of the door and then disappeared down the road.

The New Moon and the Old Moon

We all know that when the moon shines, it brightens the darkness and the darkness retreats.

Then the sun comes and chases the moon, cutting it away with its knife, little by little, until only the backbone remains for us to see.

The moon then goes home in discomfort but, after only a few days, it recovers to become a new moon and feels as though it has been reborn.

The moon again begins to move across the sky, until it becomes round and bright and the sun arrives to chase it off again.

The Hare Who Got Married

A young hare seemed unusually happy so the fox asked him, why?

'I'm married,' replied the hare.

'Congratulations! What a good luck,'said the fox.

'Not really good luck: she is old and as ugly as a witch!' 'Oh what a bad luck!' cried the fox.

'Not really bad luck : for she gave me a beautiful house as a gift....'

'What a luck!'

'Not really luck,' the hare went on, 'the house has burnt down!'

'What a bad luck! said the fox.

'Not really bad luck for my old and ugly wife was inside at the time!'

100

The Dog with the Little Bell

There was once a dog which had the bad habit of biting anyone who came within its reach.

For this reason, its master hung a little bell on the collar around its neck, so that everybody would be warned of the dog's approach and could take care not to get too close to its somewhat fearsome teeth and extremely powerful jaws.

The dog was very proud of its little bell and liked to boast that the tinkle of it scared men away. A wise old dog, however, warned it, 'The bell resounds to your shame not to your glory.'

The Popy's Riddle

A beautiful woman had been transformed by a witch into a poppy in a field. Each evening, she returned to normal and was allowed to pass the night at home. One morning, before she went back to the field to become a poppy again, she said to her husband: 'If you succeed in picking me, the spell will be broken.'

This was true, but how could the man recognise his wife amongst all the other thousands of poppies? The answer was simple: Since the woman had spent the night at home, she was the only poppy in the field that was not wet with dew.

The Weasels and the Mice

The weasels and the mice were at war and the mice kept on losing. They thought that this might be due to the fact that they were not well organised and disciplined and also they had no leaders. So the mice appointed some generals and to set themselves apart from the soldiers, the generals made themselves helmets decorated with long horns.

The next battle was won by the weasels again. And the mice only saved themselves by running into their burrows but the generals could not get in because of the horned helmets, so they were all eaten by the weasels.

The Donkey and the Grasshopper

A poor donkey was not happy with his voice. One summer day, while grazing in a field, he was captivated by the delightful music of the grasshopper. 'What is it that you eat that allows you to give off a sound like that?' he asked one of them.

'Dew,' answered the grasshopper, joking.

'That's what I need,' thought the donkey. So he went on eating grass with great enthusiasm for the rest of his life, especially at dawn, when it was covered with dew. His voice never changed, but luckily, nature had bestowed on him a healthy appetite.

Father Christmas's Workshop

At his workshop at the North Pole, Father Christmas works all year round to make the toys that children all over the world receive at Christmas. It is an important task and it requires not only imagination, but also skill and organisation. Fortunately, the gnomes of the North give him a hand. They are the most trustworthy of all gnomes, even if they do have some of the mischievous habits of their kind.

When everything is ready, Father Christmas loads up his sled, harnesses his reindeer and then, with a crack of his whip and his merriest laughter, he flies out into the night!

Aldebaran and the Celestial Camels

Aldebaran, the most luminous star in the constellation of Taurus, fell in love with Electra, the most beautiful star of the Pleiades and he went to ask for her hand in marriage. He had gifts of a herd of camels, but on the way he was attacked by another aspirant for her hand, Alcyon.

The fight between them is not yet over. Even now, on calm nights, it is possible to see pale blue Electra followed by red Alcyon and then by Aldebaran with his big herd of celestial camels, making up the constellation of the Hyades.

The Wolf and the Heron

The wolf had swallowed a fishbone and went to ask the heron to pull it out of his throat. 'I will reward you handsomely for your help,' he promised the heron.

The heron agreed and in an instant, put his long beak down the throat of the wolf and pulled out the fishbone. At this, the wolf thanked the heron and began to walk away.

'What about the reward you promised?' the heron shouted after him.

'What?' the wolf replied. 'You put your head between my jaws and I didn't bite if off! Isn't that reward enough?'

The Stag and the Lion

A stag was immensely proud of his majestic set of antlers. Yet, on the other hand, he was extremely dissatisfied with his slender legs and hoofs.

One day a lion began to chase him. By virtue of his speed, the stag succeeded in fleeing from the lion, but

then he ran into a thicket and his antlers caught in the branches and he was trapped.'Alas, and what a woe' thought the stag. 'How wrong I was to complain about my slender legs and delicate hoofs which have served me so well. How wrong I was to be so proud of my large antlers which are now the cause of my ruin!'

The Hare and the Frogs

A hare was berating itself for being so afraid all the time and running away from everything. He was just promising himself that he would behave more courageously in future, when a sudden noise made him run away again as fast as he could.

He came to a pool where, as soon as the frogs heard his approach, they dived into the water and hid in the mud.

'Thank goodness', thought the hare. 'That just proves that no matter how scared you are, there is always someone else who is even more scared!'

The Butcher and the Thieves

Two thieves went into a butcher's shop. While one was waiting to be served, the other one stole some sausages off a plate and passed them to his companion. The butcher noticed the sausages were missing and accused the pair of having stolen them. The one who had

the sausages swore he had not stolen them and the one who had stolen them swore he did not have them. Both told the truth, but the butcher beat them anyway.

'Whoever took the sausages can take one of these as well,' the butcher said between blows, 'and whoever has them can have one of these as well.'

The Stolen Ass

An Arabian farmer realised that his ass, which he had put out to pasture in a meadow, had been stolen. He immediately grabbed a stick and ran into the town. 'You miserable thieves!' he yelled, waving his club about in a menacing way. 'Give me back my ass, or I shall do what my father did!'

It was so frightening to see and hear him that even the thief was terrified, who came and handed back the stolen animal. While he was doing so, he asked the farmer: 'What did your father do?'

'He bought another ass!' was the reply.

The Dog, the Cockerel and the Fox

A dog and a cockerel, who met while on a journey, decided to travel together. Night fell: the cockerel went to sleep up in a tree and the dog settled down at the base of the trunk. Just before dawn, as was his custom, the cock crowed. He was overheard by a fox who rushed up and said, 'What a magnificent voice! Come down, I want to congratulate you.'

'I'm afraid I can't,' replied the cockerel. 'The doorman of this hotel is asleep and I can't come down until he wakes up.' 'I'll wake him up right now,' promised the fox. The dog leapt up, growled and the fox fled.

The Jealous Sole

Once upon a time in the sea, there was a loud argument about, which fish was the fastest swimmer. The dispute grew so bad tempered that at last some of the senior fish demanded that a race should take place to determine the matter once and for all. Amongst the competitors was the sole, a very arrogant fish, always sneering at the others. When the race was over, on this

occasion it turned out that the winner was the herring. The sole said, 'The herring that common little fish!' with its mouth twisted in jealousy. And ever since then, the sole's mouth has remained twisted.

The Cat and the Old Mouse

A black cat happened to wander into a warehouse, where mice lived.

'This is the place for me,' thought the cat. 'I'll pretend to be dead.' And the cat lay down on the ground. The younger mice ran towards it shouting, 'There's a dead cat.' But a wise old mouse stopped them

and said, 'Don't you know that a cat has nine lives?' Then the old mouse climbed up above the cat and chewed open a huge sack of flour that was resting on a large bin. The flour poured out and covered the cat, which lay still for a moment. Then there came a sneeze and out of the flour came a white cat.

114

The Boastful Athlete

There was once a very loud-mouthed and ambitious athlete who was not, however, very talented. One day, tired of being booed at by the crowd, he decided to leave and seek his fortune abroad.

When he finally returned, he was forever telling stories of his victories.

'In London,' he would say, 'I jumped so high I was out of sight. If you don't believe me, go and ask anyone who was there.'

'There is no need,' said a listener. 'Why don't you pretend you're in London and jump out of sight right now!'